RUNAWAYS VOL. 2: TEENAGE WASTELAND. Contains material originally published in magazine form as RUNAWAYS #7-12. Eighth printing 2009. ISBN# 0-7851-1415-7. Published by MARVEL PUBLISHING, INC., a subsidiary of MARVEL ENTERTAINMENT, INC. OFFICE OF PUBLICATION: 417 5th Avenue, New York, NY 10016. Copyright © 2003 and 2004 Marvel Characters, Inc. All rights reserved. $7.99 per copy in the U.S. (GST #R127032852); Canadian Agreement #40668537. All characters featured in this issue and the distinctive names and likenesses thereof, and all related indicia are trademarks of Marvel Characters, Inc. No similarity between any of the names, characters, persons, and/or institutions in this magazine with those of any living or dead person or institution is intended, and any such similarity which may exist is purely coincidental. **Printed in Canada.** ALAN FINE, EVP - Office Of The Chief Executive Marvel Entertainment, Inc. & CMO Marvel Characters B.V.; DAN BUCKLEY, Chief Executive Officer and Publisher - Print, Animation & Digital Media; JIM SOKOLOWSKI, Chief Operating Officer; DAVID GABRIEL, SVP of Publishing Sales & Circulation; DAVID BOGART, SVP of Business Affairs & Talent Management; MICHAEL PASCIULLO, VP Merchandising & Communications; JIM O'KEEFE, VP of Operations & Logistics; DAN CARR, Executive Director of Publishing Technology; JUSTIN F. GABRIE, Director of Publishing & Editorial Operations; SUSAN CRESPI, Editorial Operations Manager; ALEX MORALES, Publishing Operations Manager; STAN LEE, Chairman Emeritus. For information regarding advertising in Marvel Comics or on Marvel.com, please contact Mitch Dane, Advertising Director, at mdane@marvel.com. For Marvel subscription inquiries, please call 800-217-9158. For Marvel subscription inquiries, please call 800-217-9158. For Marvel subscription inquiries, please call 800-217-9158. **Manufactured between 9/9/09 and 9/28/09 by QUEBECOR WORLD INC., ST. ROMUALD, QC, Canada.**

PREVIOUSLY...

Teenager Alex Wilder and five other only children always thought that their parents were boring Los Angeles socialites, until the kids witness the adults murder a young girl in some kind of dark sacrificial ritual. The teens soon learn that their parents are part of a secret organization called The Pride, a collection of crime bosses, time-travelling despots, alien overlords, mad scientists, evil mutants and dark wizards.

After stealing weapons and resources from these villainous adults (including a mystical staff, futuristic gauntlets and a genetically engineered velociraptor named Old Lace), the kids run away from home and vow to bring their parents to justice. But when the members of The Pride frame their children for the murder they committed, the fugitive Runaways are forced to retreat to a subterranean hideout nicknamed the Hostel. Using the diverse powers and skills they inherited, the Runaways now hope

RUNAWAYS

TEENAGE WASTELAND

"Teenage Wasteland"

Writer: Brian K. Vaughan
Pencils: Adrian Alphona
Inks: Craig Yeung

"Lost and Found"

Writer: Brian K. Vaughan
Pencils: Takeshi Miyazawa
Inks: David Newbold

Colors: UDON's Christina Strain with Brian Reber
Letterer: Virtual Calligraphy's Randy Gentile
Cover Art: Jo Chen
Assistant Editor: MacKenzie Cadenhead
Editor: C.B. Cebulski

Collections Editor: Jeff Youngquist
Assistant Editor: Jennifer Grünwald
Book Designer: Carrie Beadle
Creative Director: Tom Marvelli

Editor in Chief: Joe Quesada
Publisher: Dan Buckley

RUNAWAYS created by
Brian K. Vaughan and **Adrian Alphona**

#7

How do you think we convinced everyone in California that *Alex* murdered the young woman *we* sacrificed?

You... you framed your own *son*?

Desperate times, Mr. Dean. For added measure, Alex has also been implicated in the "kidnapping" of the Hayes' girl.

And to broaden our dragnet even further, we implicated Nico Minoru and Gertrude Yorkes in these crimes as well.

But what about my child? Who's looking for *her*?

We didn't want civilians to be able to connect all six of our families, so we opted not to involve your daughter or the Steins' son in this conspiracy.

We'll wait to create cover stories for their disappearances until enough news cycles have passed

But how much time do we *have*? Chase took the Fistigons from our workshop. He's in possession of the most powerful gauntlets ever invented!

That's nothing, Stein. My Gertrude is running around with a bloody *velociraptor* genetically engineered to obey her every command.

What about *Nico*? My baby has the Staff of One now, the... the very mystic instrument that made the Dread Dormammu tremble!

You don't seriously think they'll use those weapons *against* us, do you? I mean, we're their *parents*.

Molly, get off of Gert's dinosaur! You're gonna hurt yourself!

And stop using the word "freaking" so much. It's freaking me out.

Arsenic says I can use any words I want to now, Alex. She says I don't have to do anything my *Mom and Dad* told me to do ever again.

First of all, her name is *Gertrude*, not "Arsenic". And secondly--

Gertrude is my *slave name*, Alex.

You can keep calling yourself whatever your evil parents named you, but the rest of us are *starting over*.

Right, Bruiser?

Right, Arsenic.

Aren't codenames supposed to be *cooler* than your actual names?

How's the code-breaking going, brother?

Slowly but surely.

I translated some of the first chapter, but I think it's mostly historical stuff. Whoever wrote this thing keeps talking about these weird six-toed giants called *Gibborim*.

Yeah, I'm pretty sure I've heard that word before, but I'd need a good search engine to confirm it.

Guess we're S.O.L. without D.S.L.

How about you, Chase? You and Karolina hide our wheels somewhere?

, in *plain sight.*

I stole the plates off a Honda Civic and switched them with the ones on my van. It'll be months before that dude notices he's got the wrong license on his car.

Wait. *What?*

I warned you, send him to sell our cow and he'll come back with *magic beans*

Food can wait, Molly. We haven't even figured out our next move against The Pride, and now Nico has something *inside* of her.

Well, at least *one* of us does. I'm with Bruiser. We haven't eaten in, like, twelve hours.

Maybe he's right, Alex. I'm... I'm probably just hungry.

Either way, what are we supposed to do? Call *Domino's*?

We can't use our credit cards or make ATM withdrawals without alerting the entire world to our whereabouts, and we only have nineteen bucks between us in cash.

Dude, your parents' fancy-pants lifestyle has made you *soft*. Nineteen bucks is enough to buy six people a *feast* at the local Circle A.

Fine. But if we're leaving the Hostel, we're going as a *group*. I don't want you coming back with any more magic beans.

Magic *what*?

Gert, stay here and keep an eye on Molly, will you?

Hey, why do I have to stay? I'm a *mutant*, 'member? I'm stronger than all you guys combined!

Don't worry, kid, if they forget to bring back Slim Jims for us, Old Lace here will teach them a lesson about the *food chain.*

RRRRR

#8

Sorry, guess my interests are a little more... *retro* than yours.

How *old* are you guys, anyway?

Well, *Bruiser* is our youngest. She's eleven. She's back at The Hostel with Arsenic, who's fourteen or fifteen, I think.

Alex, Sister Grimm and I are all sixteen.

Oh, same here.

Believe it or not, Talkback up there is the elder statesman of our crew.

Yeah, I remember sixteen...

...back when life was *simple*.

uld you
a snack,
offrey?

I came down
o fix myself some
rm milk, and noticed
t the neighbors had
eft a *bundt cake*
on our porch.

"We were so sorry to hear
about Alex on the news, but
everyone in the neighborhood
knows that your son is innocent,
and you are all in our
prayers."

Prayers.
Lord, I sometimes
forget what a pack
of *imbeciles* we're
surrounded by.

Well, I
just got a late-
night gift of
my own.

The Pride's operative in
Robbery/Homicide e-mailed me
a few minutes of surveillance
footage taken earlier
tonight.

Really?

What
is it?

An answer to our prayers.

That's Alex! Where... where was this taken?

A convenience store in Los Feliz.

The kids are still in *California*! I thought they'd be halfway to *Canada* by now!

Do we know who they're fighting here?

A trio of thieves... new players. Whoever they are, they certainly didn't request a permit from The Pride to rob stores in *our* city.

Regardless, if the children have opted to start playing crimefighter, it's more imperative than ever that we find them quickly...

...before some two-bit hood makes an *example* out of them.

AHHH! WHAT IS IT?!

Oh, my God!

Wher[e] Arsen[

HELP ME!

I'm here! I'm here!

Gert, call off your raptor!

I'm trying! Old Lace... she's not listening to my thoughts!

Then think harder, *Arse!* She's, uhh, too heavy to budge!

Says you, wimpster...

Scooch.

Old Lace, play *nice!*

See, she isn't trying to hurt anybody. She just likes roughhousing.

Isn't that right, you big silly-head?

RrRRrr

So, you guys bring back burritos?

Topher, this is *Gert*, whose manners are only slightly better than her *pet's*.

My *name* is... never mind.

Tell me, Never Mind, does that thing always try to eat guests?

Dunno. You're our first.

...pher is one of ..., Arsenic. His ...arents are *eeeevil*.

If that's our only criteria for admission, this cave is gonna fill up *fast*.

Come on, Topher, I'll give you the nickel tour of the joint.

Yeah, I think I'll join you.

That's okay, Alex.

I've got it.

Told you this was a bad idea, bro...

Hey, can you guys do me a favor?

If Topher asks about my *powers* or whatever, could you please not mention that I'm, you know...?

An alien?

Shh! I don't want to make him any more freaked out than he already is, okay?

Topher doesn't need to know I'm not... not from this *planet*. If he says anything, just tell him I'm a *mutant.*

Why? You know we'd accept you even if you were from *France*, Karolina! You shouldn't be--

God, I'm just asking you to do *one thing,* Chase!

You don't have to be such a...

Forget it, it's late.

I'm going to bed.

Man, this is just like the Real World... only *real.*

I'm sorry, did I--

No, it's just, there's kind of *someone else.* I don't think we're exclusive or anything yet, but we... we *kissed*, right after all of this started happening.

You and Talkback?

Eww, no!

Alex.

Really? I mean, he seems like a great guy... but not exactly the kind of boy I picture being your *type.*

He's not. Not exactly. But we've both been through the same unbelievable experience, like two people who survived a plane crash together or something, right?

There aren't a lot of guys out there who understand what it's like to discover that the people who got you a *clown* for your seventh birthday are actually *super-villains.*

Well, for what it's worth... there's one more now.

Thanks, Topher.

But I'm afraid I... I still can't kiss you.

Don't be afraid, Nico.

Why...?

Topher, *stop*.

This... this isn't right.

But you kissed me *back*.

I'm sorry, I... I don't know why.

My brain has been going in so many different directions since--

⇐ahem⇒

Everything okay up here?

Alex?

Yeah, uh, everything is--

Actually, I was just about to leave.

Topher, wait!

I should really get some shut-eye, Nico. My parents have had me on the run ever since their accident, and--

Fine, you can take a room in the *east* wing.

Nico, you and I need to *talk.*

Good luck. The last time Bruiser used her mutant mojo, she sawed logs like that for *hours*.

Speaking of which, it's almost three in the morning. When do the *rest* of you... rest?

I saw my parents kill a girl, and then I found a dinosaur in my basement.

I haven't slept in *four days*.

h, now that I'm kicking it without a curfew, I've been trying to come up with a dream schedule.

I figure I'm gonna stay up until seven A.M. every day, maybe catch the first hour of Stern before punching out, then sleep until, like... what would nine hours of Z's take me up to?

Well, if we're looking for my mom and dad tomorrow, I think I'm gonna try to get some sleep now.

See you guys later, I guess.

Hey, new kid.

What?

Don't worry about your folks.

We'll find 'em. I promise.

DANGER
GAMMA
TESTING SITE
LETHAL LEVELS OF
RADIATION

I don't know what to say, Alex.

You've been so sweet to me, and I've been acting like a total--

Nico...

No, you have to hear this. I just did something completely awful, and you deserve to--

Nico, I already know that you and Topher kissed.

You... you do?

HOW?

Oh, our first night in the Hostel, I found this *secret room* next door. It's sorta like those passage-ways in my parents'--

You've been *spying* on me?

What?

No!

I mean... not before just now.

And I wasn't spying. I was keeping an *eye* on you.

I thought Topher seemed like an okay guy, but if this stuff with our parents has taught me anything, it's not to--

I can't believe I *trusted* you!

Me?!

You know what, maybe I'm *glad* I kissed Topher.

Where are you--

⊰AWAY⊱

Nico?

HNNNNK... SHOOOOOOO...

Kill me.

GHUH... ZZZZNNN...

Gert!

My *name* is--

Have you seen Nico?

You mean Sister Grimm?

Enough with the stupid names already!

When are you going to *grow up*?

Sorry, Peter Pan.

I thought not growing up was the whole *point* of this little club.

Never mind.

I'll find her *myself*...

YUHHH!

What is *wrong* with you?

Me?! You're the one kissing *my* guy!

Your guy? What about Alex?

How many guys do you *have*?

Get off, *jerk!*

I'm not the jerk, *you're* the--

RAAAAAAR

Nico and I figured out that her body *reabsorbs* her staff after every couple of uses. Just let her catch her breath and--

ξnnnξ

Get... get away from me.

But--

I... I have to get out of this place.

Nico, hold up!

Alex, maybe you should give her some space.

Yeah, wait for--

But I... I...

Carry a torch for her? Noted.

But it's like they say, if you love something...

You see, I'm not really sixteen years old. I was born at the turn of the century.

You're *four*?

Huh?

Oh, no, *last* century. In 1900.

Eww! And I *kissed* you?

Cute.

Yeah, I got turned when I was your age. Made a small fortune in stocks after the Depression, then lost it all after the dot-com crash.

Holding up all-night liquor joints is a drag, but I've grown accustomed to a rather *expensive* lifestyle over the decades, you know?

So all that stuff you told us...

...was a *lie?* Yeah, pretty much.

I didn't want to get hauled off to ja because of some wanna super-kids, so I made that sad sack story abo my mom and dad being e

And I *knew* you'd wolf down whatever broken-home bull I fed you.

If I've learned one thing in my long life, it's that angst-ridden brats like you *always* have parent issues.

re lying.
ave some
of... of
pnotic
e. That's
we've all
n acting
strange
nd you.

No, you've been acting so strange because you're **teenagers.** You're stupid, predictable, and easy to manipulate.

But **you,** you at least have **spunk.** That's why I'm going to **turn** you... and let you help me kill your **friends.**

No...

Too bad that scary magic wand is still trapped inside your perky little chest, huh? How are you going to **stop** me?

e importantly, why would you
t to? I mean, I can give you **immortality.**

esides, it
esn't look
e you spend
h time in the
sun as is.

I... I don't want to be **evil.**

Becoming a vampire doesn't change who you are.

Growing up does that, letting the naiveté of adolescence be washed away by the cold hard water of life.

Trust me, when you've seen as much of *"humanity"* in action as I have, you start to realize that we're all just a bunch of animals.

And that means it's eat... or be eaten.

Someday, you'll understand.

When blood is shed...

...let the Staff of One emerge!

SHUNK!

AHHHHH!

OWW! *Man...* will you look at that. It went clean through me and out the other side!

But...

And what do you know, I'm already on the mend.

See, the only thing that can off me is *sunlight...* and unfortunately for you, that's about three hours away.

Sorry, kid. Whedon got it wrong.

...akes don't ...vampires, ...y just give ...eartburn.

Hey, Toph!

You're off the team.

KAFWOOM

Alex!

Where's Karolina?

Still upstairs, I guess.

Why, what's going on?

It's Topher. He's a... a monster. *Literally.*

Say what? He's part of *The Pride?*

No, I don't think he works for our parents, but he's bad. *Very* bad.

I knew it.

Old Lace smelled something funny on that guy the second he set foot in here.

RRRRRR

Well, look who came crawling back.

Old.
ace.

SIC HIM.

No need to play possum with this thing anymore, huh?

I've already learned all of your *weaknesses.*

Hup!

Uhf! Hey, Gert? Do you know what really killed all the dinosaurs?

Oh, God. **Molly.**

You... you were *awake* for that?

I thought I heard people fighting and... and then I woke up, and then Topher was kissing Lucy in the Sky's neck and then... and then...

Shh, it was just a *dream*, okay?

I miss my mom and dad!

I... I want my mommy a daddy!

I know, Molly.

I know...

#11

Molly Hayes.

You say this girl was kidnapped by *other* kids?

Yeah, three teenage runaways... Alex Wilder, Nico Minoru and Gertrude Yorkes.

Although there's a chance that, uh, *more* kids might be involved, too.

Well, there's nothing *"typical"* about these runaways. Before they went *AWOL* with *Molly*, they *murdered* an innocent girl.

Odd. In our experience, adolescents are rarely abducted by their own kind.

And typical runaways don't take off in *groups*, not unless they have similar experiences with seriously messed-up home lives... abusive parents and stuff like that.

And to make matters worse, we think a few of these freaks may have some kind of creepy *powers*.

Er, no offense, of course...

And I assure you, Dagger and I would not have come to your wretched city if we did not feel strongly about this case.

Please... I wouldn't have asked you two to travel all the way from New York if I didn't think you were the Hayes girl's last hope.

Don't mind Cloak.

East Coast/Le Coast rival die hard

So, ah, what happens now?

We do what we do, Lieutenant.

...we call yo

Don't call us...

BEEEEEEP BOP

TIEMENS

Calling....

Mr. Wild

Yes, I have good new sire. The Prid may be one st closer to havi its *offsprin* back...

Nico, if we leave the Hostel now, we risk being found.

The risk is the same if we stay in one place forever, Alex... maybe greater.

Besides, you're the one who said that we should use this stuff we took from our parents to start making up for all the *suffering* they've caused.

I know, but I can't risk anyone else getting hurt... not after what almost happened to Karolina.

I'm... I'm *okay*, Alex. Really.

But I would feel a lot better if I could, you know, punch a bad guy in the face or something.

What are we supposed to do, just head out and *look* for trouble?

We can go on patrol... like the Guardian Angels!

We don't have to take on terrorists or anything yet. We can start small, purse-snatchings and crap.

Well... I suppose we need to make a supply run anyway.

Gert, you can stay here with Molly?

You can't leave us *alone*, Alex!

What if more *monsters* show up?

The kid's got a point. I'm not sure Old Lace and I could survive any more *ampires-vay.*

All for one and one for whatever then.

Fine, you can tag along, Molly, but under *no circumstances* will you be permitted to leave the van. Got it?

Yes!

We finally get to wear ou costumes!

I'm the only one who made a costume?

Well, you'll be pleased to know that it took my lovely wife and me all of two minutes to counterfeit the new fifty.

Not that The Pride will be strapped for cash anytime soon, after I used the Spine of Agamotto to install that musclebound *lummox* as our governor.

Enough with the back-patting, already! What of our *children?*

We have yet to receive another message from whichever of the runaways is our *mole*...

...but my husband and I have devised a *plan* if and when this mysterious asset helps us locate our progeny.

Heh. *"Stark Naked."*

We should get some kinda *award* for this.

Finally... a crime in progress.

What, defacing an ad for some evil corporation that's in bed with the military industrial complex?

That's not a crime, it's a *public service.*

Come on, Arsenic! This is the first action we've seen all night. We're gonna run outta *gas* before we find something better to fight!

Knock yourself out, Talkback, but I'm not going to help you guys play *junior fascists.*

Should I put my costume on *now,* Lucy in the Sky?

Um, sure, Bruiser... as long as you promise to stay in here and help Arsenic and Old Lace guard our wheels, okay?

Awwww, what a *rip!*

Quiet, team.

Let's get into character.

Who's to blame for this, Tandy?

Children killing children. Every year, it feels as if we see more and more of it.

For what?

I don't know, Ty.

But kids have been doing awful things to each other since the *Children's Crusade*, so maybe it's just...

What is it?

Something caught my eye. A *glimmer.*

How far?

Follow me.

I'll light the way.

Capa y Daga!

Don't... don't hurt us, yo.

Piece is just a *water pistol*... see?

Vándalos.

Desaparecer o sufrir.

Alex Wilder and Nico Minoru?

You're coming with us.

How... how do you know our names? If you work for our *parents*, you can--

DROP THE WEAPON!

UHN!

Sister
Grimm

Everybody,
chill!

I...I read about
these two on the
Bugle's website.
Arm & Hammer or
something. They're
good guys, B-list
heroes from New York!

B-List?

"Popularit
isn't a concern

L.S.D.,
you take
tall dark and
ugly!

I'll
get the
chick!

Flame on, *skank!*

What did you call me?

Leave us *alone!*

Your light is my sustenance, girl.

Your body, my nourishment.

AHHH!

Hope you saved room for seconds, partner.

It's so... so *cold!*

Alex, help m--

Stop it!

I don't know what you've been told, but it's *wrong!* We're not killers, we're... we're just like you!

Tell it to Judge Ito, Wilder.

Don't you see what this is? Two groups of super heroes meet, have a stupid misunderstanding, then fight?

This routine was old when we were *born!* We don't have to--

Be silent, murderer... and enter the fold.

#12

think *we* look weird?

What's with that tty get-up, ? Don't you e any *self-espect*?

Nope, but I've got *these*.

The one with the beast is Gertrude Yorkes, no?

Yeah, she's one of he brats who idnapped the little Hayes girl.

By the ay, kid, if you on't like *this* outfit...

SHIN

...you should see my *old* one.

Old Lace, *now!*

Thanks for the cover, O.L.

Is... is she *okay?*

Yeah, just *hungry.*

Um, *problem.* My powers, they don't hav any effect o animals or--

THWAP

Dagger!

Easy, Old Lace. She's just a skinny little thing.

We don't want to break her in *two*...

Child, if you have harmed her in any way, I will kill you with my own--

STOP FIGHTING!

Just let our friends out of your ugly *cape*!

Come on, I don't wanna have to rip up your bed sheets!

This is not a "sheet", girl. It is a *cloak*, a gateway to another realm permanently bonded to my very being.

Not even a *god* has the strength to rend it from my--

UMPH!

RAHHHH!

TY!

UHN!

Puh-puh-**please.**

Guh-guh-give it buh-buh-**back** to me.

I'm rry! I thought I were another **monster.**

I didn't ow you were a **stutterer.**

You made me h-ruh-**revert** to who I was hen I fuh-fuh-**rst** donned my cloak.

My mommy is a speech therapist. Maybe **she** can help you!

Bruiser, your parents are psychotic **super-villains.**

Oh, yeah.

I keep forgetting...

Super-villains?

What are you two *talking* about?

Yeah, our *folks.* The people who duped you into coming after us.

No, the *police* asked for our help.

Same diff. They're all in it together, part of something called "The Pride". They murdered a chick and framed *us* for the crime.

But the little girl you guys *kidnapped*...

How blonde *are* you?

That's Molly Hayes!

Aww! You ruined my secret identity!

See, we didn't *kidnap* anybody. We *rescued* her.

Oh, my God. Then your pals... *they're* innocent, too?

And now they're tr-tr-trapped in the Duh-Duh-Darkforce Dimension.

Th whe nov

Nnn.
Her knives...
her knives showed me my sins...

Nico's delirious.

Chase, can you use your Fistigons to build us a campfire?

I... I think the buste dude

It's our powers. They don't work here.

I'm not an *alien* in this place. I'm... I'm just a regular--

WHHOOOOOOOOO

What was *that*?

This is real

C

It can't be...

When Molly ruh-ruh-ripped my cloak from me, she suh-suh-severed my connection to your friends.

It was an accident! I didn't know it was a *magic* cape!

What do you mean they're *lost*?!

Hold on, I have to wrap my brain around this.

This guy's outfit is like the mystical equivalent of a portal to the internet, but the server crashed, so before I can perform a *search*, we have to find a way to get back online...*right?*

That was the worst analogy I've ever heard... but it gives me an idea.

My light daggers have a *purifying* quality. If I pump Ty full of them, I might be able to *repair* his link to Creepsville.

There's a duh-duh-danger of *overdose*, but it's our only huh-huh-*hope*.

Close your eyes, ladies.

This is gonna be bright...

...but it might not be *pretty*.

GAH!

Everybody... in one... *piece?*

You.

You sent us to *Hell.*

Hands off, Talkback. We don't need any more meaningless punching.

Yeah, then what *do* we need?

The only thing our kind dreads...

Dialc

Hey, [yo]u guys are [any]**thing** but [c]owards.

Me and Cloak didn't have **half** your guts and street smarts when **we** ran away from home.

Hn.

Well, I guess we should head back to our... place. Can we give you a ride somewhere or--

Thanks, Alex, but I think we'll rest here until we've gotten enough juice back for our jump to NYC.

You just keep taking good care of your team, okay?

Hang in there, Molly! This is all gonna be over soon!

Thanks!

It was awesome to meet you, Cloak and Dazzler!

My **name** is...

I hate this city.

BZZBZZBZZ

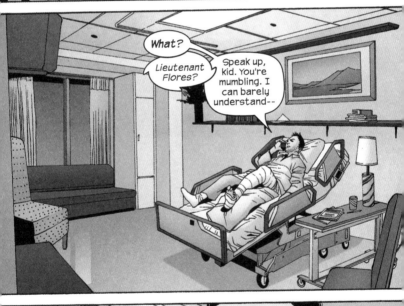

What?

Lieutenant Flores?

Speak up, kid. You're mumbling. I can barely understand--

You're the dork who sent Cloak and Dagger after us, right? I'm surprised our parents haven't killed you yet.

Who... who *is* this?

Right now, I'm the only friend you've got.

You're one of their *children*, aren't you?

The Pride told me they might have a *mole* in your gang, but I didn't believe--

Quiet. I don't have long. I'm at a payphone outside some taco shack, and the others think I'm in the bathroom.

What do you--

Listen, Cloak and Dagger are on a rooftop in Van Nuys, but I'm not sure how much longer they'll be there.

Lieutenant, they *know* about The Pride.

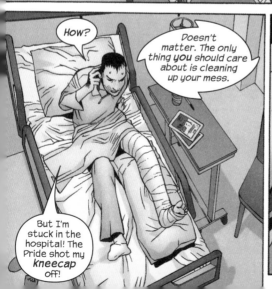

How?

Doesn't matter. The only thing *you* should care about is cleaning up your mess.

But I'm stuck in the hospital! The Pride shot my *kneecap* off!

Do *something*... or the next bullet will probably be to your *brain*.

ave it to Stein to suggest erimentation. Still, I have qualms, so long as it's just on *humans*...

Hold them eady, Frank. If we se one incorrect napse to fire, we uld lobotomize them both.

On my count, dear. One, two...

AHHHHHH!

Are ey...?

No. Merely unconscious. I believe we have...*success*.

They'll wake up confused and disoriented, but they shouldn't remember anything from the last twenty-four hours.

I'll plant a suggestion in their subconscious to make them attribute the blackout to *binge drinking*. That should confuse the little teetotalers...

We haven't t that close since nder Man incident years back. We're ky our *"deep throat"* led when he... or *she* did.

I still don't get it. If one of our runaways is really *loyal* to us, why not call us *directly?* Or at least tell us where they are?

Yes, who in *God's* name is our mole...?

"...and what are they digging up for us?"

Next: The Good Die Youn